PR

AERONAUTICA:
Collectables relating to military and naval airforces of the world 1914–1984.

*An Illustrated reference guide
for collectors*

A.J. Marriott-Smith

ARMS AND
ARMOUR

First published in Great Britain
in 1989 by Arms and Armour Press, Artillery House,
Artillery Row, London SW1P 1RT.

Distributed in the USA by Sterling Publishing Co. Inc.,
2 Park Avenue, New York, NY 10016.

Distributed in Australia by
Capricorn Link (Australia) Pty. Ltd., P.O. Box 665,
Lane Cove, New South Wales 2066, Australia.

British Library Cataloguing in publication Data:
Marriott – Smith, A.J.
  Aeronautica: collectables relating to military and
  naval airforces of the world 1914–1984–
  (Illustrated reference guides for collectors)
  1. Militaria
  I. Title II. Series
  355.8
  ISBN 0–85368–939–3

Typesetting and origination by Best-set Typesetter Ltd, Hong Kong
Printed and bound in Great Britain by
The Amadeus Press Ltd, Huddersfield, West Yorkshire

INTRODUCTION

Aircraft and their intrepid pilots are a truly 20th century phenomena. The world's newspapers of the early 1900's carried banner headlines recording the latest achievements of British, American and Continental aviators (and a few aviatrix): Orville Wright, Colonel Cody, Monsieur Bleriot etc. Bleriot's first channel crossing captured the public imagination, souvenirs of the aircraft and items commemorating flights and achievements were rapidly produced to satisfy public demand, collecting Aeronautica had begun!

This collectors handbook will cover mainly the military aviation material of two world wars. The actual subject is vast and specialist books cover most subjects in depth. However, the academic author is not concerned with the value or availability of his subject, only its purpose, design or effect.

This handbook is for the collector and indicates the actual cost and rarity of the items he collects.

I apologize for the fact that World War One aviation, my major interest, is somewhat more favoured than others.

ACKNOWLEDGEMENTS

I would like to thank the following for their generous help and assistance in the compiling of this book.

Mr F.J. WILKINSON – without whom the book would never have started.
Mr MIKE LLEWELLYN – of the Hawkinge Battle of Britain Musum.
MAJOR GARY PERKINS – U.S. Airforce.
Mr TERRY MOORE – Photographer
Mrs WYN WARREN and Mrs MELANIE JAMES for endless typing and corrections.
KENT SALES, Auctioneers, for use of their premises, time and photographic records.

BIBLIOGRAPHY

There are thousands of books dealing with all things aeronautical so I have listed some useful *basic* reference books and collectors journals. With the aid of this type of literature most enthusiasts should find a starting point for their chosen area of specialisation.

Collectors Journals

"Cross & Cockade". U.K. journal of 'Society of WWI Aero Historians' Cragg Cottage, The Cragg, Bramham, Weatherley. W. Yorks. LS23 6QB
"Over the Front". U.S.A. journal of 'The League of WWI Auction Historians' Editor: G.H. Williams, 39745 Better Drive, Dallas, Texas 75229. U.S.A.
"Fly Past". Monthly magazine covering all aspects of aviation. Key Publishing 1 Worthorpe Road, Stamford, Lincs. PE9 2JR

Books

A Short History of the Rc. Air Force, Air Ministry (1936).

Angolia, John. R., *The Luftwaffe Air organization of the Third Reich*, Bender Publishing (1972).

Imperial Japanese Army & Navy Uniforms and Equipment, Arms & Armour Press (1987).

Bowen, Ezra, *Knights of the Air*, Time-Life Books.

Bruce, J.M. *British Aeroplanes 1914–1918*, Funk & Wagnell (1957).

Chalif, Don, *Military Pilot & Aircrew Badges of the World 1870 – Present*, Vol. 1, Bender Publishing.

Greerer, Louise & Harold, Anthony, *Flying Clothing*, Air Life (1979).

Lewis, Peter, *Squadron Histories RFC, RNAS & RAF 1912–59*, Putnam Ltd (1959).

Marzetti, Paolo, *Tenute Di Volo Della 2 Guerra Mondiale*, Albertelli (1983).

Mason, Francis K. *Battle over Britain*, McWhirter Twins (1967).

Rawlings, J. *Fighter Squadrons of the RAF and Their Aircraft*, MacDonald & Janes (1969).

Robertson, Bruce, *Air Aces of 1914–18 War*, Harleyford Publications (1959).

Rosignoli, Guido, *Airforce Badges & Insignia*, Blandford Press (1976).

Badges & Insignia WWII Airforce-Naval-Marine, Blandford Press (1983).

Smithsonian Institution, National Air & Space Museum. *Aircraft in Museums around the World*, Smithsonian Institution (1979).

Sweeting, C.G. *U.S. Combat Flying Clothing*, Arms & Armour Press (1984).

Weld, J. *Flying Headgear of the World 1934–45*, California, USA (1980).

Woodhouse, Henry, *Text book of Military Aeronautics*, T. Werner Laurie Ltd, U.S.A. (1919).

THE WHERE AND HOW TO
BUYING AERONAUTICA

Auctions

Local auction sale rooms provide a rich source of material, be nice to your local auctioneer and you will find he will be able to point you in the direction of bargains.

Major sale rooms such as Sotheby's, Christies, Phillips etc., all have regular sales of Aeronautica. Do not be put off by the fact they handle World record paintings etc, they do sell collectors items to 'mere mortals'. In fact, many collectors are often amazed at how reasonable prices are at these sale rooms. The only rules when buying at auction are to *always* read the catalogue description fully and *always* view the lots you wish to purchase.

Air Shows

Most air shows held during the Summer months have 'aerojumble' stalls. Both the professional dealers and enthusiastic collector will be there at Biggin Hill Air Show, Duxford 'Flying Days' or The Shuttleworth Collection 'Flying Days' etc. These are the true enthusiasts 'happy hunting grounds' and the best place for meeting fellow collectors.

Adverts

A modest size advertisement in your local newspaper for 3–4 weeks consecutive editions under the *WANTED* section of Classified adverts, will often bring amazing results.

Reproductions and Fakes

'Caveat Emptor' (Buyers beware) is advice often quoted but not too often followed. Remember that most collectors have 'champagne taste' but only 'beer money'. This means that dealers are asked for rarities that are seldom available; rather than disappoint the customer, some will obtain facsimiles.

There are no hard and fast rules in identifying fakes or reproductions; common sense is your main advantage. If you are offered the 'Red Baron's' flying helmet or Douglas Bader's Control Column, there is only a million to one chance of them being authentic. Collectors should always realise that knowledge is the most important aspect of collecting. Better to spend time in museums studying artifacts or buy good reference books, than to start your collection with a worthless imitation!

In recent years reproductions have become so accurate that they sometimes appear better quality or more 'authentic' than originals. Solid silver badges of both the Nazi Luftwaffe and U.S. Airforce are produced in America. The quality in some cases is better than the original. India and Pakistan now produce facsimile bullion wire embroidered insignia that is almost impossible to fault. This is small wonder since they now have the contracts to produce the ornate full dress scarlet tunics and embroidered insignia of Her Majesties Brigade of Guards!

PRICE GUIDE

A price guide in any area of collecting is unlikely to be totally accurate. Conditions of items can vary greatly, as can the owner's interpretation of conditions. It is normally accepted that the person selling an item grades it at least one grade higher than the buyer. With prices it should be remembered that values fluctuate with market variables. Overseas buyers will pay higher prices, in general, at auction than the U.K. buyers. However, if the foreign currencies drop in value against sterling, then the collecting market often follows suit. Sometimes market supply exceeds demand and the prices plummet. An example recently was the film 'Top Gun' which caused a World-wide demand for U.S. Naval flyers leather jackets. The prices rocketed from an average of £100 to £300–£500, and reports of people being 'mugged' for their jackets hit the news. 'Top Gun' fever subsided and now jacket values have reverted to normal.

Auction prices are usually a good market guide to values, but even these prices can sometimes become exaggerated if two or three collectors decide they want one rare item. The price will exceed normal commercial levels and will reach a new record high price thus setting an unrealistic precedent.

As a rule of thumb, if you wish to obtain a good collection which will be both a pleasure and an investment. Always:

1. Buy the best example you can find.
2. Never rush into a purchase.
3. If in doubt over value or authenticity, dont buy.
4. Buy from a 'good' source, a reputable dealer or auction house.

VALUES

1. UNIFORMS: FLIGHT, SERVICE & DRESS

1. Tunic £175–£250 Side Cap £75–£100 Sam Browne £20–£30
2. £150–£200
3. RAF Tunic & Cap £80–£100; U.S. Tunic & Cap £100–£150
4. £75–£100
5. £150–£250
6. Flight jacket (Scarce) £150–£200 Oxygen mask (Very scarce) £150–200 Helmet & goggles £100–£120
7. Flight Suit £100–£125 Oxygen mask (Very scarce) £150–£200 Helmet £90–£100 Parachute (Scarce complete) £175–£250 'Mae West' £125–£175
8. Suit £200–£250 Helmet £90–£120 Life Jacket £50–£75 Watch £80–£90 Boots £100–£150
9. Complete £300–£350
10. Helmet £90–£100 Jacket £175–£225 'Mae West' £50–£75 Compass £40–£50
11. U.S. jacket £100–£150; French tunic £75–£100
12. £300–£400 complete
13. £350–£400 complete
14. £200–£300
15. £90–£120
16. £75–£85
17. £75–£85
18. (Very Scarce) £350–£450
19. £100–£150
20. £175–£300
21. £125–£150
22. £50–£60
23. £200–£300
24. £175–£250
25. £150–£250
26. £125–£150
27. £100–£125
28. Tunic £125–£150 Helmet £200–£250 Sword Belt £50–£75
29. £150–£175
30. £300–£400
31. 'B' type Helmet (Scarce) £150–£200 'D' type Oxygen mask (Rare) £300–£350 Irvin Harness (Rare) £150–£200 B.D. top & Trousers £75–£80 Boots £85–£100
32. 'B' type Helmet (Scarce) £150–£200 Mark IV Goggles £75–

£80 'D' type Mask (Rare) £300–£350 Green 'Mae West' 1932 pattern (Rare) £275–£350 Parachute (Scarce complete) £150–£175 Boots £85–£100
33. Tunic £100–£150 Flight Coat £100–£150 Full hood Helmet £150–£175 Swagger Stick £20–£30
34. £75–£100
35. Goggles £60–£80 Helmet £100–£150 Flight jacket £150–£200 Gauntlets £50–£100 Fug Boots £100–£200 Thornton–Pickard camera gun £250–£400

2. EPHEMERA

1. £100–£150
2. (Rare) £350–£500
3. (Scarce) £150–£200
4. £40–£50
5. £200–£250
6. £20–£25
7. Depending on service details £50–£500
8. £80–£120
9. £25–£30
10. £25–£30
11. £25–£30
12. £20–£25
13. £30–£40
14. £20–£25
15. £20–£25
16. £25–£50
17. £15–£20

3. ESCAPE ITEMS

1. £95–£125
2. £75–£100
3. £75–£100
4. Box of 12 £50–£60
5. With Compass to base. £35–£50
6. £35–£50
7. £25–£30
8. £20–£25
9. £25–£40
10. £20–£25
11. £60–£100
12. £25–£30
13. £50–£75
14. £25–£30
15. £100–£200

4. BADGES AND INSIGNIA

1. (Scarce) single titles £25–£30 matching pair £70–£90
2. (Rare) £200–£250
3. (Scarce) pilots single £25–

£30 pair £75–£100 observer single £20–£25 pair £50–£75
4. (Scarce) £50–£60
5. (Scarce) £45–£50
6. (Very Scarce) £70–£80
7. (Commemorative patches are scarce but not greatly collected) £15–£20
8. £5–£10
9. £15–£20
10. £5–£10
11. £8–£12
12. £7–£10
13. £15–£20
14. £5–£10
15. £5–£10
16. £5–£10
17. £10–£15
18. £5–£10
19. £15–£20
20. £10–£15
21. £10–£15
22. £15–£20
23. (Scarce) £75–£100
24. £20–£25
25. £20–£25
26. £7–£10
27. £25–£30
28. (U.S.) £20–£25
29. £10–£15
30. £20–£30
31. (Scarce) £80–£120
32. (Very scarce) £100–£150
33. £100–£150
34. £175–£200
35. (Scarce) £150–£200
36. (Scarce) £175–£225
37. (Very scarce) £100–£150
38. £90–£120
39. £100–£200
40. £175–£250
41. £50–£75
42. £25–£40
43. £30–£50
44. (Very rare) £150–£200
45. (Scarce) £800–£1200
46. (Rare) £300–£500
47. (The price varies on which grade and whether with pendant.) £60–£120
48. £60–£120
49. (For standard bronze and silver award – Rare) £500–£600
50. £25–£40
51. £30–£40

5. 'AERODROME ART' SOUVENIRS AND PRESENTATION ITEMS

1. £25–£30
2. £25–£30
3. £150–£200
4. £50–£75
5. £45–£60
6. £100–£150

7. (Value increased if inscribed to or from an interesting pilot.) £50–£60
8. (Value increased if inscribed to or from an interesting pilot.) £30–£50
9. £50–£200
10. £250–£400
11. £50–£70
12. £50–£75
13. £100–£150
14. £40–£50
15. (Depending on age and condition) £100–£200
16. £25–£40
17. £150–£200
18. £300–£400
19. £75–£100
20. £50–£75
21. £35–£50
22. £70–£90
23. £50–£150
24. £30–£40
25. £25–£100
26. £25–£40
27. £75–£100
28. £25–£40
29. £125–£175
30. £100–£125
31. £50–£75
32. £150–£200
33. £45–£50
34. (Scarce) £100–£125
35. (Value depends on whether H.M. silver or plated) £50–£200
36. £80–£100
37. (Scarce) £100–£125
38. £30–£40
39. £45–£60
40. £25–£30
41. £35–£45
42. £75–£100

6. GUN SIGHTS, CAMERA GUNS, CONTROL COLUMNS AND AIRCRAFT REMNANTS

1. (Very scarce) £200–£250
2. (Scarce) £100–£150
3. Gunsight (Unique) £750–£1000   Adler magazines £5–£8   Cuff title £60–£80
4. £75–£80
5. (Very scarce) £250–£350
6. (Scarce) £150–£200
7. (Very scarce) £200–£250
8. £100–£150
9. (Rare) £350–£500
10. (Unique) £500 +
11. (Scarce) £250–£350
12. (Unique) £1000–£2000
13. £75–£100
14. £200–£300
15. £125–£150
16. £300–£400
17. £90–£120
18. £100–£150
19. £75–£100
20. £300–£400
21. £100–£150

7. EDGED WEAPONS

1. (Scarce) £250–£300
2. (Scarce) £150–£200
3. £90–£120
4. £150–£250
5. £125–£150
6. £200–£250
7. £100–£150
8. (Rare) £150–£200
9. £80–£120
10. (Scarce) £175–£225
11. £100–£150
12. £150–£175
13. £100–£125
14. £100–£125
15. £75–£85
16. £150–£200
17. £200–£250
18. £75–£100
19. £150–£200
20. (Scarce) £100–£120
21. £90–£100
22. (Scarce) £275–£400
23. £90–£120
24. (Rare) £850–£1000
25. George V. (Scarce) £200–£250   Edward VIII (Rare) £350–£500   George VI £200–£250   ERII £200–£250   Air rank Officers £250–£350

8. GOGGLES

1. £50–£75
2. £30–£40
3. £25–£35
4. £35–£40
5. £40–£50
6. (Scarce) £75–£100
7. (Scarce) £75–£100
8. £45–£60
9. £40–£50
10. £30–£40
11. (Value increased if issue marked and dated) £30–£80
12. £75–£100
13. £50–£75
14. £50–£60
15. £50–£60
16. (Rare) £150–£200
17. (Rare) £100–£150
18. £50–£60
19. £40–£45
20. £30–£40

9. PICTURES, PHOTOS AND PORTRAITS

1. £170–£180
2. £200–£250
3. £100–£125
4. £40–£50
5. £50–£75
6. £45–£60
7. £90–£125
8. £25–£30
9. £50–£75
10. £75–£100 each
11. £100–£125
12. £75–£85
13. Print Version £45–£60

14. £75–£100
15. £150–£175
16. £200–£300
17. £75–£100
18. £90–£100
19. £60–£80
20. £100–£150
21. £15–£20
22. £100–£150
23. £20–£25
24. £20–£25

10. HEADWEAR, DRESS AND FLIGHT

1. Value increases with addition of Owners name, Squadron insignia kills etc.) £125–£175
2. (Value increases for camouflaged version, plus addition of unit, Squadron or Owners name etc.) £100–£125
3. £100–£125
4. (Scarce) £100–£150
5. (Scarce) £60–£80
6. (Scarce) £75–£100
7. (Value increases if containing an interesting Owners name) £40–£45
8. (Value increases if containing an interesting Owners name) £60–£75
9. (Value increases if containing an interesting Owners name) £90–£125
10. £80–£100
11. £45–£60
12. £90–£120
13. £45–£60
14. £50–£60
15. Helmet £95–£125   Goggles £70–£80
16. £150–£175
17. £140–£160
18. Full size £145–£160   Miniature £60–£80
19. (Very rare) £250–£400
20. £200–£250
21. £150–£175
22. £150–£175
23. £150–£175
24. £150–£175
25. Helmet (condition is very important) £80–£150   Goggles £90–£120
26. Helmet £70–£90   Goggles £90–£120
27. Helmet (Scarce) £150–£200   Mark IIIA Goggles £80–£120   'D' type Oxygen mask (Rare) £300–£350
28. 'C' type Helmet. (Value varies on condition and whether with earphones etc.) £30–£50   Mark VII Goggles £25–£35   'G' type Mask £25–£35
29. 'D' type Helmet £60–£90   Mark IVA Goggles £75–£80   Oxygen Mask £75–£100

10

1. UNIFORMS: FLIGHT, SERVICE & DRESS

1

2

1. WWI Royal Flying Corps. 2nd Lieutenant's wrap–over service Tunic (known as the maternity jacket). Khaki whip cord material with two external pockets. Matching side Cap and Sam Browne belt and holster. This pattern Tunic was often worn on patrol and in combat as well as for ceremonial duties. **2.** WWI Royal Flying Corps. Officers khaki service Tunic of Army pattern. Cuff rank insignia. Length-of-service Chevrons to right sleeve (red or blue colouring denoting Home or Overseas service.). Brass RFC buttons.

3. Left, a WWII RAF Tunic with Warrant Officer sleeve badge and a Polish Pilots Badge above the wings; right, a WWI U.S. Army Aero Unit Tunic of 3rd pursuit squadron. **4.** WWII Italian Facists Airforce Officer's 4 pocket Tunic, having cuff rank insignia. Eagle pilots wings and breast pocket badge of an Interceptor fighter squadron. **5.** Nazi Luftwaffe Pilots Flight Jacket having embroidered Pilots proficiency Badge to left side. Luftwaffe eagle to right side. Sleeve rank insignia (Oberfeldwebel). Blue/Grey material with fur collar.

6. WWII Nazi Luftwaffe Pilots brown leather Flight Jacket, having embroidered breast eagle. Map pocket to chest. Fur trimmed collar and Lieutenant rank shoulder straps. Oxygen mask, flying helmet and goggles. **7.** WWII Nazi Luftwaffe Bomber pilot flight Uniform. Summer weight one-piece overall with sleeve rank insignia (Oberfeldwebel), having matching Summer-weight cloth flight helmet with leather microphone covers, oxygen mask. Parachute back-pack and kapok-filled "Sausage" pattern Life Jacket. **8.** WWII Nazi Luftwaffe Winter-weight all-leather flight suit. The leather version worn by Air crew having to fly over sea. With sheepskin-lined leather helmet. Fighter pilot pattern Life Jacket. Large size issue wrist-watch, and standard pattern flying boots.

9. Luftwaffe Pilots Winter-weight Flight suit. Over-land pattern, having Summer-weight helmet. Standard issue Goggles and Flight Boots.   **10.** WWII Nazi Luftwaffe fighter Pilots Flight Uniform. Summer-weight brown mesh netting and leather helmet. Blue/grey gaberdine Jacket with blue velveteen collar. Fighter Pilot Life Jacket. Lapel fixing compass.   **11.** Left, a WWII U.S. Army Air Force officers service jacket with U.S. pilots insignia and RAF pilots wings; right, a WWI French officers 4 pocket service tunic.

12. British Inter-wars period, Summer Flight Uniform of University of London Air Squadron. White cotton Flight Helmet with Luxor style goggles, and having 'Gosport tube' in-plane communication ear phones and tubing. One-piece flight suit Overall. Blue embroidered insignia to left pocket. c.1936 **13.** RAF Pilots Summer-weight Flight Uniform (1926–35). Tan leather flight helmet. Mark II pattern goggles. White one-piece Overall flight suit. Bullion-embroidered Pilots wings. Sheepskin Flight Boots.

14. British Pre-WWII Civil Air Guard Pilots Uniform. Leather helmet. Private purchase Luxor-style Goggles. Grey 4 pocket Overall flight suit, with C.A.G. buttons and sleeve insignia. c.1938. **15.** British Inter-wars Pilots flight Suit. Brown leather helmet. Mark IV Goggles. One piece Sidcot suit with detachable fur collar. **16.** RAF WWII Sergeant Pilots service Uniform: Side cap, 4 pocket Tunic, with Pilot wings and S.D. trousers.

17 **18** **19**

17. WWII British RAF Bombardiers Battledress Uniform. Slip-over rank title of Flying Officer. Air crew whistle to collar. (Used for attracting attention when shot down and in dinghy). Matching combat trousers and side hat. **18.** WWII British Pilots electrically-heated Irvine suit, for high altitude flights. Early pattern helmet and Mark III Goggles. Sheepskin-lined Jacket and trousers. Special pattern flight Gloves and leather Boots. **19.** WWII U.S. Army Air Force Officer's Uniform. Chocolate brown, peaked service Cap with gilt cap badge. Tunic with gilt insignia. Silver navigators wings and 2nd pattern USAAF shoulder insignia. Normally worn with 'Pinks' (a particular shade of distinctive service dress trousers).

20. The ubiquitous 'Irvine' jacket, standard RAF air crew issue in WWII, brown leather, sheepskin-lined. Much prized after WWII by motorcyclists and sports car owners. Good examples are hard to find.   **21.** Pre-WWII Wing Commanders full dress parade tunic with embroidered bullion-wire pilots wings, gold wire and lace trim decoration.   **22.** WWII USAAF officers chocolate brown 'Ike jacket'. Wire-embroidered pilots wings, 2nd pattern USAAF sleeve patch, 5 gilt bar service stripes to sleeves.   **23.** U.S. Naval pilots brown leather flight jacket c.1958. Goatskin, fur collar, embroidered with pilots name and wings 'Fleet Aero Gunnery Unit' sleeve badge and 'VA-55' War Horses, V 55 Benninton Badge to reverse. These jackets are fashionable with the 'macho' and seldom survive in good condition.

24. U.S. Naval pilots one-piece leather flight suit, with fur collar, electrically heated. **25.** U.S. Naval pilots brown leather flight jacket with painted insignia of 'Flying Tigers' and '1st Pursuit Squadron'. (Many of these original jackets having modern painted motifs added to enhance their value). **26.** USAAF Pilots jacket 'A.2' pattern brown leather flight jacket. **27.** USAF Generals Service Uniform, having pilots wings for fixed wing aircraft, helicopters and missile expert gadge. c.1970. **28.** British RAF Wing Commanders full dress tunic, helmet and sword belt with slings. The distinctive helmet is of black leather with fur trim, blue and gold corded and has distinctive grey/blue feather plume. c.1938.

29

30

31

32

29. WWII Luftwaffe officers full dress cape, with silver wire eagle to left side fastening chain and Eagles head mounts. This could be worn with all uniforms and even over the great coat! **30.** WWII Nazi Luftwaffe 'Pilot Instructors' uniform (Gruppenfluglehrer der Luft-kriegschulle), peaked service cap, 4 pocket tunic with markmans lanyard, pilots badge NSFK glider pilots insignia. Notice the moth damage to lower section. This can devalue a uniform to the extent that it is eventually stripped and just the insignia displayed. **31.** British RAF 1939/40 Period Air Gunner/wireless operators flight Uniform. 'B' pattern Helmet, 'D' type oxygen mask, Irvine Harness Suit, B.D. top and trousers, all-leather flight boots. **32.** RAF 'Battle of Britain'-era pilots flight uniform, 'B' Helmet, Mark IV B Goggles, 'D' type mask, Green Mae-West, Seat parachute Harness, B.D. top and trousers, canvas and leather boots.

33. RFC pilots tunic, leather flight coat, full hood Helmet and Swagger stick. **34.** WWI Women's Royal Air Force Cap and Tunic. (WRAF was formed April 1918). **35.** Observers Flight Clothing c.1917: RFC Goggles. Tinted glass lenses, sprung cloth and fur trimmed backing; RFC issue Tan leather standard flight Helmet; RFC issue flight Jacket in tan leather, blanket lined, with angled map pocket; 'Otter' fur flight Gauntlets; Suede and sheepskin 'Fug' Boots; carrying a 'Thornton-Pickard' camera Gun with 'Lewis' gun top magazine.

2. EPHEMERA

1. USAAF airmans photo album scrapbook together with his medals awards and citations.
2. Interesting collection of paperwork and research relating to Lt. R. Applin RFC, his officers commission, photo portrait, service log book, bronze death plaque. Research revealed this officer was shot down by the 'Red Baron'.

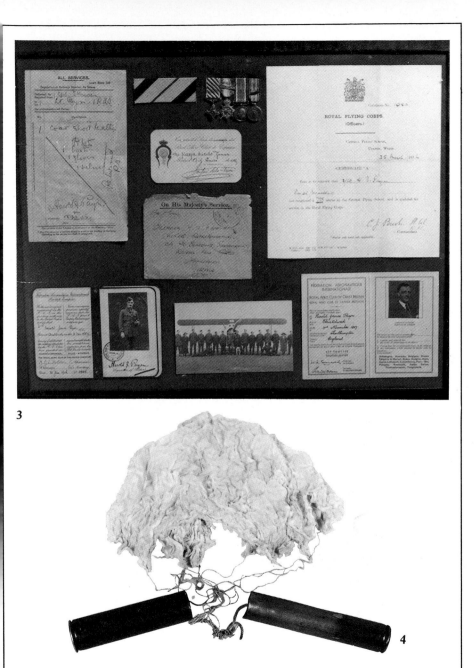

3. Collection of ephemera relating to Sqn. Leader H.J. Payn RFC, comprising his Royal Aero club flying license, service book, RFC flying certificate, group of 4 WWI miniature medals including A.F.C. Mons Star, War and Victory Medals with an M.I.D. clasp. **4.** British RFC message cannister, made from 2 shell cases and with silk parachute attached. Used for dropping urgent messages to ground-based forces.

5. Group of 4 WWI medals awarded to Lt. L.D. Brown RFC: Air Force Cross, 1914–15 Star, WWI silver War and gilt Victory Medals. **6.** RFC airmans photo portrait and frame. **7.** RAF pilots service log book. **8.** Group of 4 items relating to Luftwaffe 'unter offizier'. Comprising his service flying license, an NSFK flight details book, Luftwaffe glider pilots license and log book plus grey linen active service 'Ausweis'.

9. Nazi NSFK membership card, used as identification and for recording membership dues. **10.** Luftwafe 'glider pilot' license and log book. **11.** DLV members Ausweis. **12.** Pre-Nazi era I.D. card and 'Dauerkarte' for entry to Berlin airport. **13.** D.V.L. Ausweis for an officer 'Luftsportfuhrer'! **14.** WWI membership card for an aeroclub and flying school. **15.** Nazi era Lufthansa personal I.D. card. **16.** Nazi Ausweis dated 1935 for service at an Airport and Airship centre. **17.** Membership card for German light aircraft club.

3. ESCAPE ITEMS

1. Pair of RAF 1940 all-leather flight boots of 'Escape' pattern, having been designed to allow upper section to be detached leaving a pair of 'civilian' style shoes. This was to allow aircrew the opportunity to utilise their boots when attempting to escape or evade capture.   **2.** Pair of RAF 1943 pattern 'Escape' boots, having suede and sheepskin lined upper section. This pattern boot was also supplied with concealed saw or knife blade inside upper section lining.   **3.** 1943 pattern with a detached upper section.

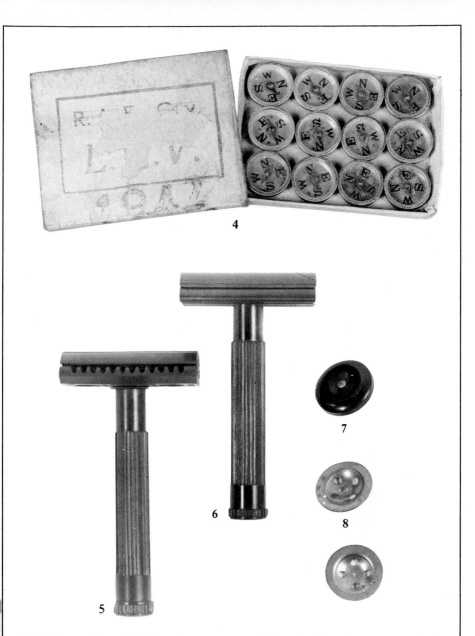

4. RAF 'stores' box of 12 'Escape' compasses, small size, issued as shown, or concealed in buttons, razor bases, etc. These continued in service for sometime after WWII. **5.** WWII British forces razor in brown bakelite, this pattern often contained a compass to the base when sent in Red Cross parcels to P.O.W's. **6.** Similar razor. **7.** RAF air crew 'Fly button' compass, black bakelite standard pattern button but having magnetised centre with luminous paint dots to flat surface. When suspended from thread it would rotate as per standard compass. **8.** RAF air crew 'Fly button' compass, 2 piece brass button type one button having raised spike to centre, the other with magnetised centre and luminous markings.

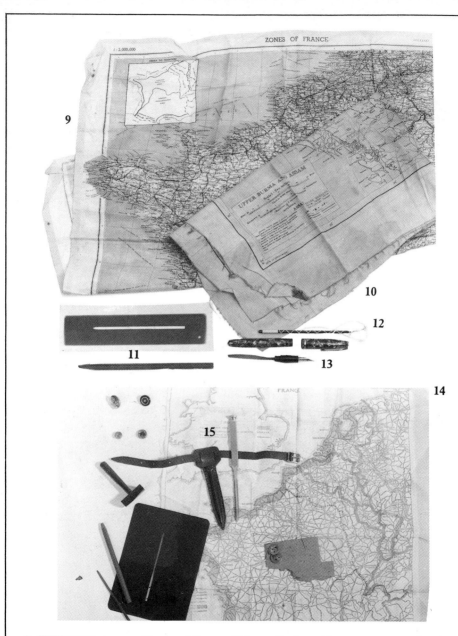

9. WWII RAF air crew silk map of France. This usually showed best escape routes, frontiers etc. These were sometimes issued seperately and at other times within a complete 'escape' kit. **10.** WWII RAF air crew silk map of Burma and Assam. **11.** Navigators 'war economy' blue wax crayon pencil with concealed blade similar to 12. **12.** Standard blade for concealment also utilised by SOE and OSS operatives. Blued steel with hollowed triangular section blade. **13.** Standard fountain pen, containing single edged utility blades. **14.** WWII RAF silk 'escape' map of France. **15.** An S.O.E. issue wrist dagger with sheath.

4. BADGES AND INSIGNIA

1. Pair of Royal Flying Corps shoulder Titles, white cotton embroidered on blue backing.
2. WWI Austro-Hungarian Pilots Badge embroidered in metallic and coloured thread on white backing for Summer uniforms. This pattern insignia was worn by pilots of the Hungarian Naval Air service 1917–18. 3. WWI Belgian Air Corps. collar insignia for pilot and observer, white metal construction. 4. WWI French Air crew badge of unofficial 'private purchase' pattern for 'Bombardier'. Silver with pin-back fastening. 5. WWI Austrian Air Service Pilots collar insignia of 'Balloons', brass finish. 6. WWII British RAF 'Air Ministry Constabulary' cap Badge in 'war economy' white plastic. Secured by folding brass clips to reverse. 7. Unusual squadron 'Commemorative' flight-suit Patch. 8. RAF 1939 pattern 'brevet' half-wing with letter 'S' denoting 'Signaller'. 9. RAF 1939 brevet, 'A.G.' denotes 'Air Gunner'. 10. Engineer.

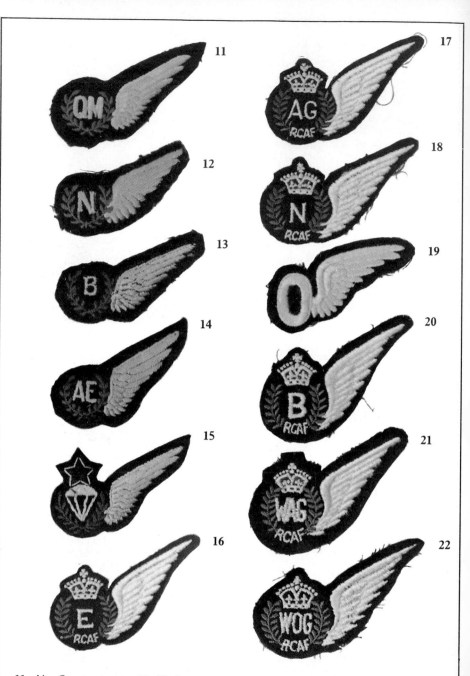

11. Air Quartermaster. 12. Navigator 13. Bomb Aimer. 14. Aircraft Engineer. 15. Senior parachute Instructor. 16. Royal Canadian Air-force Engineer. 17. RCAF, Air Gunner. 18. RCAF Navigator. 19. RAF Observer. 20. RCAF Bombardier. 21. RCAF Wireless – Air Gunner. 22. RCAF Wireless Operator – Gunner.

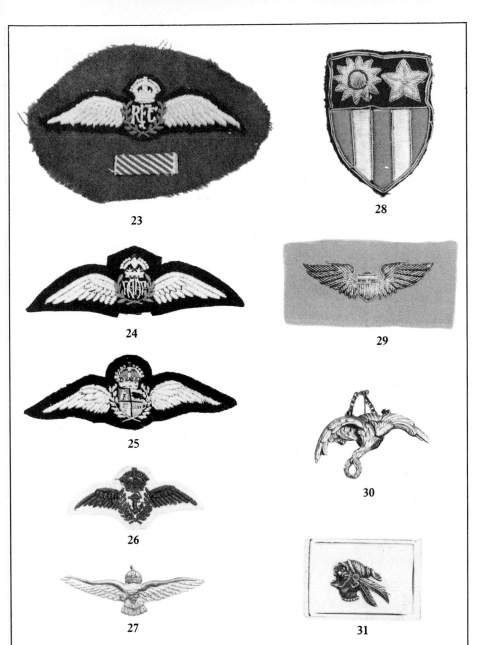

23. WWI Royal Flying Corps Pilots wings with A.F.M. medal ribbon, all attached to portion of uniform material. **24.** WWII Royal Australian Air Force pilots Wings **25.** WWII South African pilots Wings. **26.** WWII Fleet Air Arm pilots Wings, blue embroidery on white material worn on lower section left sleeve. **27.** Hungarian Air Force pilots Wings. **28.** U.S. South East Asia Command shoulder Insignia. C1942 **29.** U.S. Pilots Badge, silver wire embroidery on tan (summer tunic) material. **30.** WWII Polish Free Forces pilots Badge. **31.** U.S. WWI Aero Squadron Badge, private purchase from 'Tiffany's. For 213th squadron.

31

32. WWII 'Free Czechoslovak' Air Force pilots wings in silver and gilt. Manufactured by Spink & Son, London.   **33.** WWII F.C.A F. Pilots 'Honour Award' in gilt washed zinc complete with presentation case embossed with inscription to Wing Commander W H Wetton on 10th July, 1945.   **34.** WWII Nazi Luftwaffe Observers Badge, complete in its case of issue. **35.** Pre-WWII Nazi NSFK 'Balloonists' proficiency award, metallic wire embroidered for flight suit wear.   **36.** WWI German Naval Observers award in gilt finish.   **37.** Pre-WWII Japanese aeronautical award in orginal fitted case. Awarded to both foreign and Japanese recipients who contributed to Japan's aeronautical services.

38. Nazi NSFK bronzed alloy award plaque for participation in the 1938 'Deutschlandflug'. **39.** Nazi Luftwaffe pilots proficiency award, found in varying quality from solid silver through to zinc. **40.** WWI Imperial German Air Force observers award in silver and enamel. **41.** Royal Flying Corps Pilots Wings. **42.** Japanese Naval air crew/personnel wings for enlisted men, cotton embroidered with metal star. **43.** Japanese Naval pilot, Officers proficiency wings, metallic wire embroidery on blue backing, gilt overlaid star. **44.** Rare Royal Flying Corps, Naval pattern, Cap Tally. Gilt wire embroidery on black silk band. Believed to be one of only 80 produced for RFC Naval Wing.

45. German airforce 'Honour Goblet' first created in WWI and awarded to airforce personnel in recognition of their first confirmed aerial combat victory. WWI version was made in iron, alpaka and silver. The Nazi version was instituted by Hermann Goering in 1940, this was an unofficial award given to Luftwaffe personnel who had received the Iron Cross 1st class but whose performance and service did not qualify for the German Cross or Knights Cross. **46.** A pair of silver beakers bearing the personal crest of Hermann Goering, note the similarity in design to 45. **47.** Luftwaffe 'Operational flying clasp' (Frontflug – spange) for Bomber air crew. This example has a pendant attached below which signifies additional missions flown totalling 400 in all. **48.** Luftwaffe clasp for reconnaisance and Air Sea Rescue squadrons. Awarded in 3 grades: bronze for 20 flights, silver for 60 flights and gold for 110 flights. **49.** The Hermann Goering *'Commemorative medal of the German Academy for Aeronautical Research!'* **50.** Nazi Wehrmacht Anti-Aircraft 'Flak' unit badge, created in 1941 and awarded on a points system. 16 points for an award, 4 points were awarded for downing an enemy aircraft. It could also be awarded, without the points system, for an act of bravery. **51.** *Nazi Luftwaffe Anti – Aircraft 'Flak' unit badge.* One grade in silver grey finish, awarded in a similar system to the Army version.

5. 'AERODROME ART' SOUVENIRS AND PRESENTATION ITEMS

1. WWII Brass model of the Nazi 'Doodlebug' – VI Rocket. Made from bullet and shell cases. 2. WWII Brass model Bi-plane utilises shell casing and shell bases for wheels! 3. An amazing WWI RFC Squadron 'Gong' utilising the barrels, piston rods and extended magazine from a Lewis gun. The two suspended barrels give off a resonant note when struck. 4. An unusual and scarce WWII RAF Padres active service Bible and Communion set for 'Field Services'.

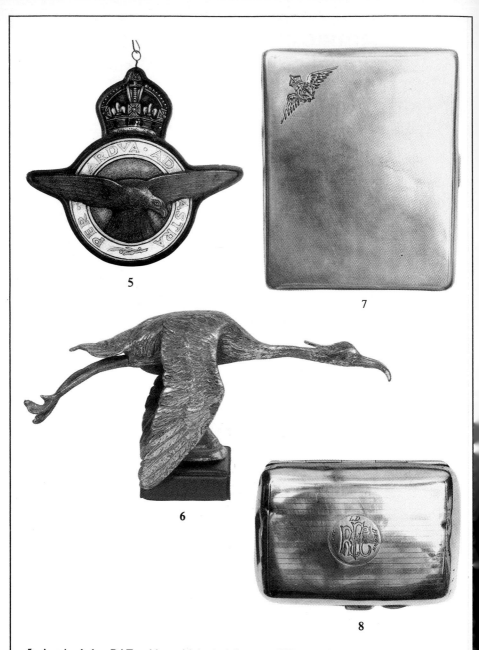

5. A stained glass RAF emblem with lead edging.   **6.** WWI-era nickel-plated brass car Mascot of a Heron in flight. The insignia, adopted by French fighter squadrons 'Escadrille 167' and others of the 'Cigognes' group, was also used in 'Hispano-Suiza' motor cars.   **7.** Hall-marked silver Cigarette Case with 'RAF' wings to one corner, often inscribed with Owners name and squadron etc. Always check the Hall-marks to ensure they are period items!   **8.** WWI RFC Officers Cigarette Case inscribed with Owners name.

9. WWI souvenir 'propeller' Clocks. These were produced in their thousands and varied in quality from the plain to the exotic. **10.** An impressive bronze, being a representation of the WWI R.F.C. Home Defence Squadrons.

11. A presentation etched brass plaque from RAF 42 squadron (Torpedo Bombers), having facsimile signatures of pilots around the squadron crest. The border displays the unit base names Donibristle (1936), Thorney Island (1937) etc. **12.** Hand-painted RAF fighter Squadron crest on Air-craft canvas for 56 Squadron ('Punjab' squadron) who flew Hurricane/Spitfires and Typhoons. **13.** R.A.F. Officer's Full-dress 'Busby' style Helmet, with incorrect pattern feather plume. **14.** Intersquadron challenge cup which held one gallon of beer and was used in drinking matches. **15.** R.A.F. Band drum, minus top skin, c.1920. **16.** An 'official' colour print portrait of R.A.F. Airmarshall Trenchard. As displayed in R.A.F. Headquarters, Mess halls etc.

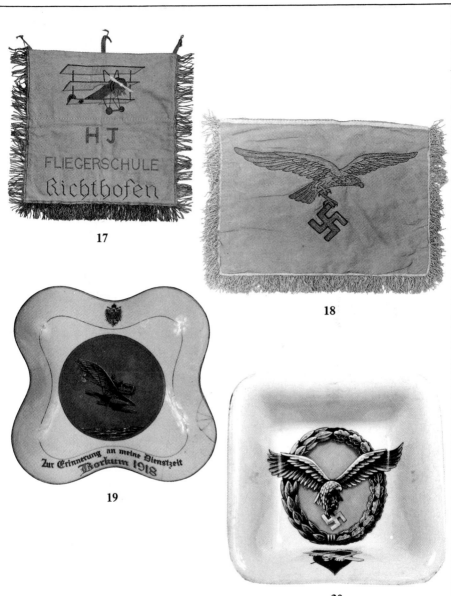

17

18

19

20

17. Nazi era 'Hitler Youth' trumpet Banner for 'Fliegerschule Richthofen' depicting the 'Red Baron's' Fokker Tri-plane. Silk thread embroidery and metallic fringing. c.1936. **18.** Nazi Luftwaffe trumpet Banner of the 'Fliegerhorst kommandantur Berlin-Gatow'. Measures 13″ × 19″, yellow banner with gold wire embroidery. **19.** Imperial German Commemorative wall Plate for Marine See-flieger unit at 'Borkum'. Imperial German forces were very 'souvenir' minded and vast quantities of Beer Steins, pipes and plates were produced to show the owners patriotism and service details. **20.** A similar commemorative wall Plaque for a Nazi pilot serving with a 'Tank Buster' squadron of fighter Bombers.

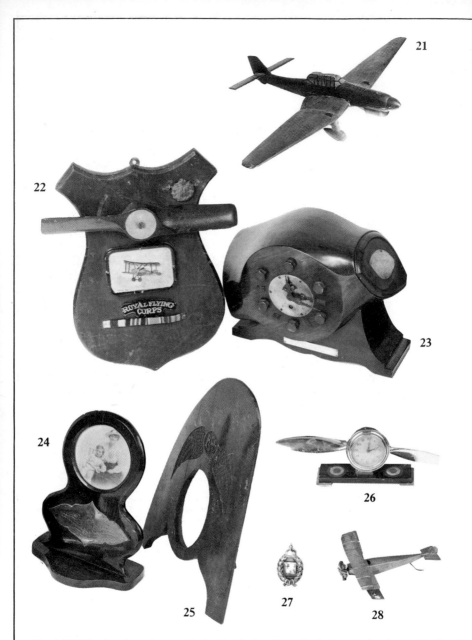

21. A WWII painted wooden model of a Nazi Luftwaffe Ju 87 'Stuka' dive bomber. **22.** Royal Flying Corps souvenir shield having cap badge, small propeller, picture and RFC title. **23.** A WWI RFC propeller Clock with presentation plaque. **24.** Wood and brass picture frame. **25.** A WWI RFC propeller tip photo frame. A very popular WWI souvenir and varying in quality from plain to work of art. **26.** WWII propeller Clock in nickel-plated brass with transfer roundel decoration. **27.** WWI Imperial German Air-force Observers Badge converted to a menu holder!. **28.** WWI German made model aircraft.

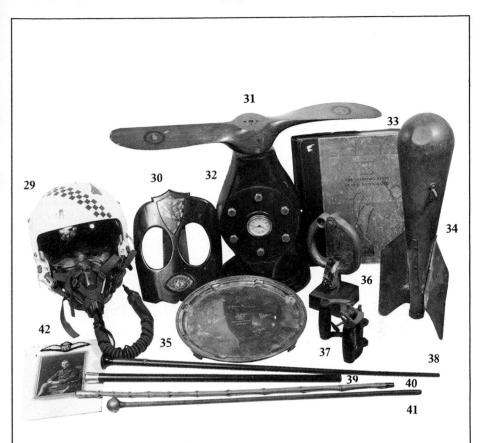

29. USAF pilots Helmet from the Vietnam war era; worn by an F111 fighter pilot it has twin sliding visors and 'Dayglo' Insignia to the dome. The various helmet decoration is useful for instant aerial I.D. **30.** WWI era propeller twin photo frame, unusual in retaining the makers trade logo's 'Langs propeller works' and 'Morris & Co.'. Propellers or propeller souvenirs which retain the makers transfer logo are scarce. **31.** WWI German aircraft generator propeller, 27″ overall length, retains the makers transfers for 'Intergrade BS9B', patent DRP. **32.** A propeller Clock of vertical type with silver presentation plaque. 'With the compliments of No.8 squadron RNAS'. **33.** Air Ministry manual 'Notes on the Interpretation of Air Photographs'. This large book is a goldmine of information for WWI aero enthusiast who own the usual selection of Aerial Battlefield Photos. **34.** Royal Flying Corps practice bomb, 20″ in length, of 1916 pattern with triple fins and a single 'D' ring air-craft rack fitting. This one is dated 1917. **35.** Silver Salver, with presentation inscription and facsimile autograph signatures of pilot's from 769 squadron in 1944. **36.** British RAF fighter aircraft control column, retains 'Fire' button but minus safety catch. **37.** WWI Firing mechanism and grips for the Vickers .303 water-cooled machine gun. **38.** RFC Officer's swagger stick, polished wood with small alloy 'wings' attached. **39.** RFC swagger stick; H.M. silver top engraved with RFC wings and owners initials. **40.** RFC swagger stick of the most common pattern, having embossed white metal top and cane haft. These have been reproduced in quantity during 1970's. **41.** RFC swagger stick; H.M. silver 'ball' top and leather covered haft. **42.** Photo portrait of an RFC pilot with his original embroidered 'wings'.

6. GUN SIGHTS, CAMERA GUNS, CONTROL COLUMNS AND AIRCRAFT REMNANTS

1

2

3

4

1. The reflector gun-sight fitted in Nazi Luftwaffe fighter aircraft, Messerschmitt Bf109, Focke-wulf 190 etc. **2.** RAF issue reflector gun-sight fitted to the Spitfire and Hurricane. **3.** The reflector gun-sight from Nazi Luftwaffe ace Werner Molders' aircraft, together with a copy of 'Adler' bearing a portrait of Molders (official photo magazine for Luftwaffe personnel), and a portion of squadron cuff title. **4.** 2 patterns of oxygen breathing apparatus fitted to Nazi Luftwaffe fighter Me 109E. Normally manufactured by 'Draeger', these are connected by oxygen tubes to the face masks.

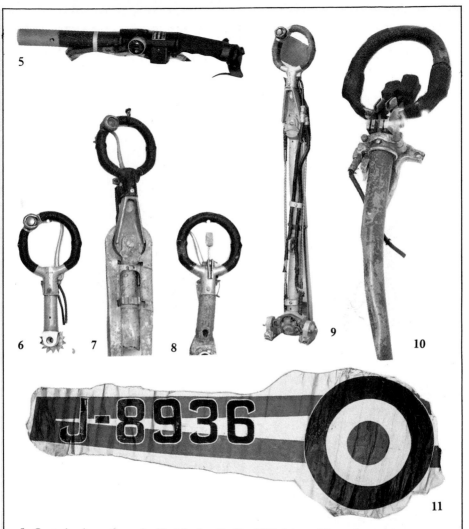

5. Control column from the Nazi Luftwaffe Me 109E fighter. The makers plaque attached normally had the issue number, date of manufacture and other useful information enabling the enthusiast to trace the individual aircraft. This column was removed from an aircraft shot down in the Battle of Britain, 1940.   6. A control column with firing button for the RAF 'Hawker Hurricane' WWII fighter aircraft; this single button fired all 8 machine guns. The columns are normally in alloy with black cord binding and brass 'Fire' button.   7. Control column and upper assembly section from an RAF 'Spitfire' fighter aircraft. These are scarce collectors items and few survive in good condition. During WWII they seldom survived crashes as due to the aircraft's design they were normally badly damaged by the dash board.   8. RAF fighter control column circa 1936 having central firing lever.   9. Complete control column and mechanism from an RAF 'Spitfire'.   10. Gloucester Gladiator control column with twin push firing levers which controlled 4 guns (2 in nose and 2 on wings). This column was removed from an aircraft flown and crashed by Wing Commander R. Stanford Tuck D.S.O., D.F.C. whilst with No.65 'East India' squadron.   11. Portion of aircraft fabric, silver finish paint with red 'V' strip, retaining its RAF roundel and plane number. It was removed from an RAF Armstrong Whitworth 'Siskin' fighter aircraft. c.1930.

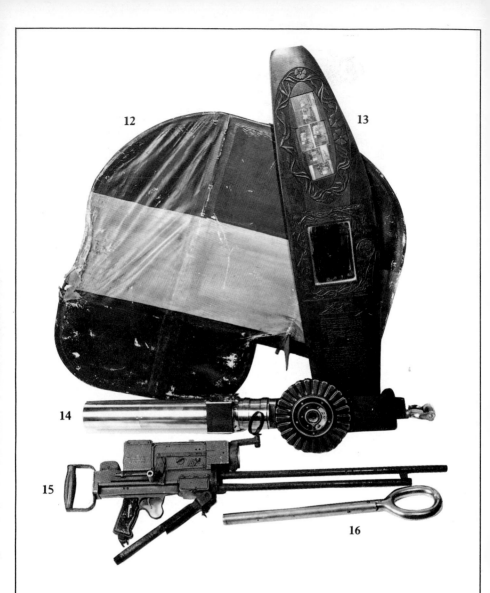

12. A complete WWI RFC Tailplane from a Bristol Scout fighter aircraft. This is of metal rod construction, having a covering of unbleached Irish linen with doped and red/white/blue painted finish. The makers 'Bristol' logo and issue numbers are to the side. This tailplane was removed from an aircraft crashed by RFC 'Ace' Albert Ball.   **13.** WWI half propeller blade with photo's inset, mirror, carved battle honours etc.   **14.** An RAF issue 'Thornton-Pickard' camera gun, simulating an aircraft Lewis gun. The magazine to the top is non-operational, the trigger mechanism operates camera and film. These were used both for aerial combat training and normal aerial photography.   **15.** An RAF issue 'Williamson' camera gun. Fitted with Dallmeyer telephoto lenses, AM issue markings No.14A/874, it has a side cocking action. **16.** Royal Flying Corps aircraft control column in brass and nickel plated steel. Marked with A.I.D. inspection marks and issue serial No.2373. c.1914.

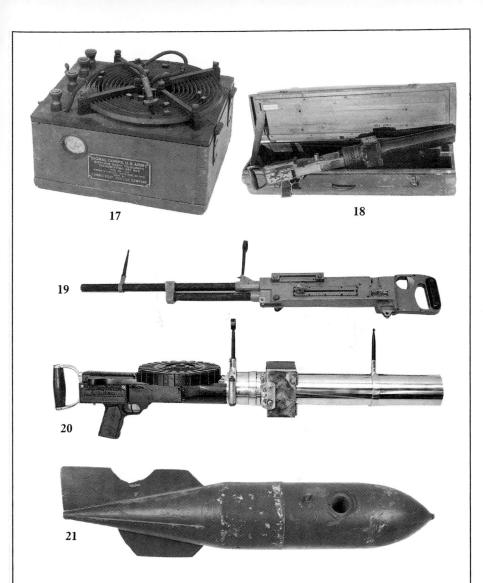

17. WWI U.S. Aero squadrons Radio transmitter, wooden cased with makers plaque to side dated 1918. Used for transmitting ranging instructions to Artillery units, its main disadvantage was the length of aerial needed to transmit and the problems caused by leaving the aerial trailing when manouvering or landing! **18.** An RAF 'Thornton-Pickard camera gun, complete with its wooden storage and transit case in 'untouched' condition and minus its dummy magazine. Note the makers label to the corner of the lid. **19.** RAF issue cine-camera gun, electrically operated on 12 volt system. The AM issue plaque is marked 'Mountin type 29 12 volts' and has stores reference 14A/1382. Grey and matt black paint finish. Note the unusual trigger position! **20.** A magnificant example of a 'Thornton-Pickard' camera gun model, type GIII. Complete with magazine and correct pattern sights of ring and bead, the outer casing is polished to bright brass, although service models were black paint finished. **21.** Nazi Luftwaffe bomb, 50 kilo size High Explosive type with alloy casing, fins damaged and fuze removed. Drab green paint finish.

7. EDGED WEAPONS

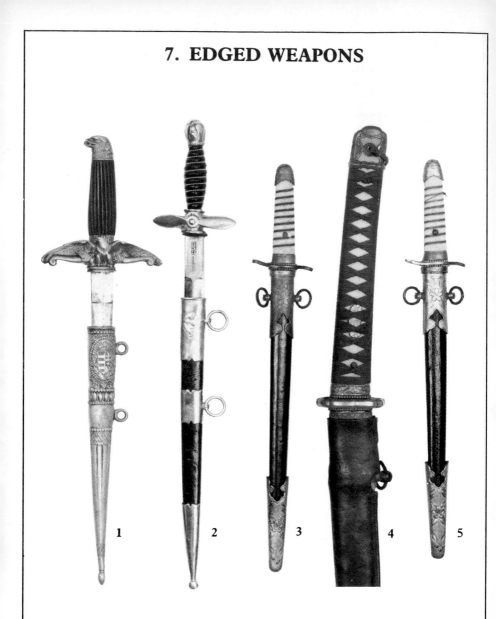

1. Hungarian air-force Officers dress Dagger. It is from the inter-war and Nazi-occupation period, having brass mounts and scabbard with ribbed wood grips.   **2.** Yugoslavian air-force Officer's dress Dagger of the late 1930's. With blue leather covering to the grip and scabbard, it was often found with Nazi made blades.   **3.** Japanese Naval Aviators dress Dagger, late war pattern with plastic hilt and scabbard mounts with dark bronze metallic finish. The same dagger was worn by both Naval Officer's and Naval Aviators.   **4.** Japanese WWII Army Aviators dress Sword of standard Army pattern with leather field service scabbard cover. Most pilots favoured the 'Wakizashi' or short sword (blade length 12″–24″) as this made it easier to fit into the cockpit!   **5.** Japanese pre-WWII Naval Aviators dirk with gilt brass mounts and fittings.

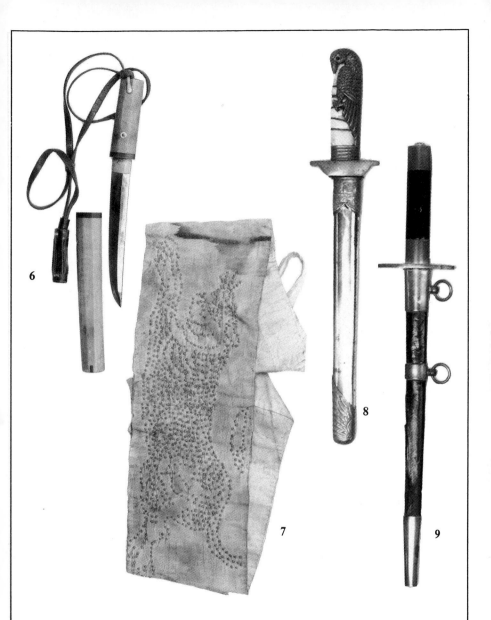

6. Japanese 'tanto' Dagger carried by 'Kami-Kaze' pilots who would commit seppuka as they dived onto the target ship. The blade is mounted in 'shira-saya' mounts of wood, this was to ensure that the ornate fittings and mounts of the dagger were undamaged by blood. The leather thong/sword knot was for wear around neck. **7.** 'The belt of 1,000 Stitches' (Senninbari) worn by 'Kami-Kaze' pilots; each knot was made by a well wisher and sometimes coins would be sewn into the belt to help 'pay the way' into the hereafter. **8.** Unusual Chinese Nationalist airforce Officer's dress Dagger. Brass mounts, plated scabbard with Chinese airforce motif to base mount. **9.** WWII French air-force Officer's Dagger with blue composition grip and blue leather covering to scabbard.

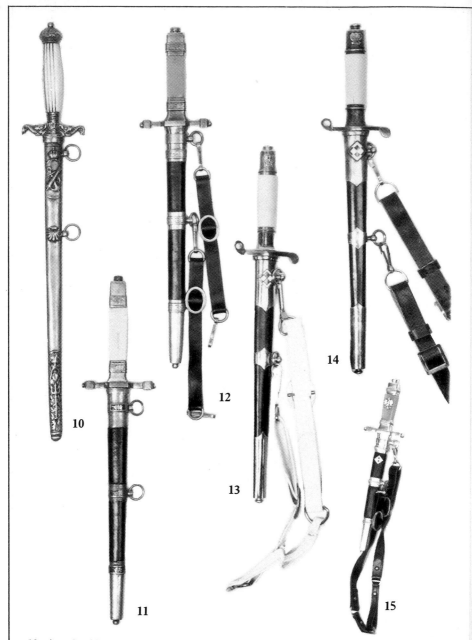

10. Austrian Naval Officer's dress Dagger; worn by Naval Aviators it has brass mounts and ribbed ivory grips. **11.** Polish Army Aviators dress Dagger of early pattern with ivory grip and brass mounts. **12.** Polish 'Honour' dagger with yellow ivorine grips, plated mounts and retaining its suspension straps. **13.** Polish airforce 'Observers' dress Dagger, of postwar manufacture complete with Summer parade wear suspension straps. **14.** Similar dagger with black suspension straps. **15.** Miniature version.

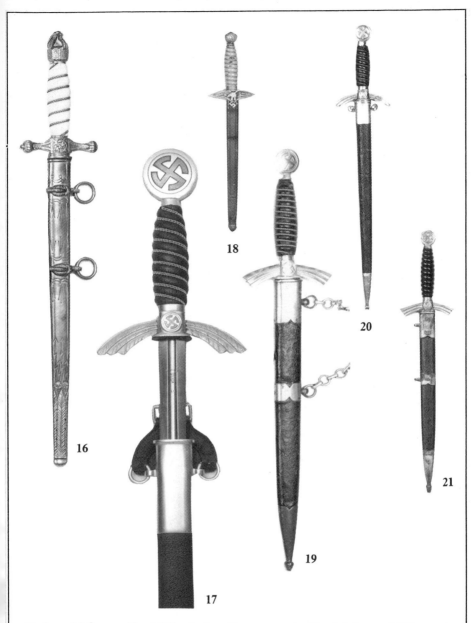

16. Imperial German Naval Officer's dress Dagger worn by Naval Aviators of Officer rank. Brass scabbard, Imperial 'crown' pommel. **17.** Nazi Luftwaffe Officers dress Sword. It has silvered mounts with gilt swastika motifs, blue leather covered grip and scabbard and was styled on the early 'Knightly' Sword of the 14th century. **18.** Miniature version of the Nazi Luftwaffe Officer's 2nd pattern dress Dagger. These miniatures were given as advertising gifts to personnel and Officers in positions to recommend manufacturers. **19.** Nazi Luftwaffe 1st pattern Officers dress Dagger. **20.** Miniature version Nazi Luftwaffe Sword. **21.** Miniature version Nazi Luftwaffe 1st pattern Dagger.

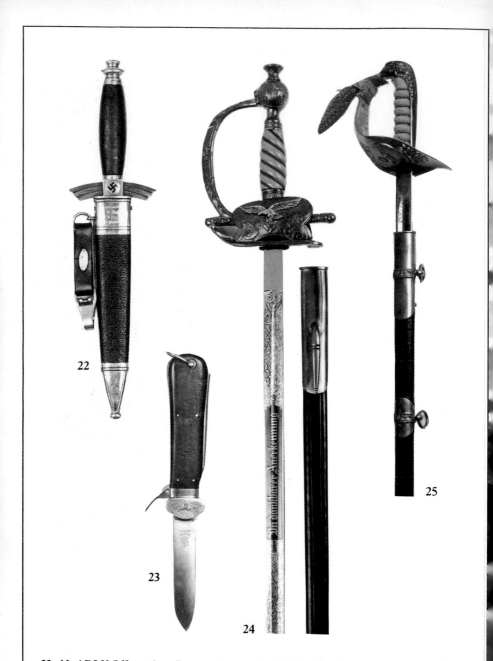

22. Nazi DLV Officers dress Dagger also worn by NSFK.   **23.** Nazi paratroopers and air crew 'gravity' knife, utility model knife with stainless steel single edged blade and 'spike' to reverse.   **24.** Luftwaffe General's Sword by Carl Eickhorn.   **25.** British RAF Officer's dress Sword, the pattern remained unchanged through four monarchs reign's (George V, Edward VIII, George VI, Elizabeth II). The only difference being the monarchs cypher to guard and blade. Officer's of air rank wear the same sword but with more ornate scabbard mounts.

8. GOGGLES

1
2
3
4
5
6
7
8
9
10
11

1. Luftwaffe manufacturers card box for flight goggles, contains a pair of spare plain glass lenses, a pair of tinted lenses and cleaning materials. **2.** Standard pattern Nazi Wehrmacht issue goggles, also worn by motorcyclists and A.F.V. personnel. **3.** German 'Lietz' pattern with white rubber surround; variations of this goggle were privately purchased for both aero and motoring usage, being popular from 1930–1940. **4.** Similar goggles but with larger lenses. **5.** 'Uvex' pattern goggles, worn by NSFK glider pilots and Luftwafffe. **6.** Luftwaffe issue 'Nitsche and Gunther' shatter proof goggles, with elasticated strap and plain lenses. **7.** Similar pattern but with tinted lenses, normally in Amber colouring. **8.** RAF issue Night simulation goggles worn by pilot and airgunners. **9.** RAF Night training goggles, stores reference 22C/1041, 1942–45 issue density style lenses which simulated moonlight viewing during daylight flights. **10.** RAF MkVIII goggles with tinted lenses, stores reference No.22C/930. **11.** RFC and RAF MkII pattern goggles used from WWI through to the 1930's. Metal framed, with triplex lenses, they have sprung cloth eye surrounds and elasticated strap.

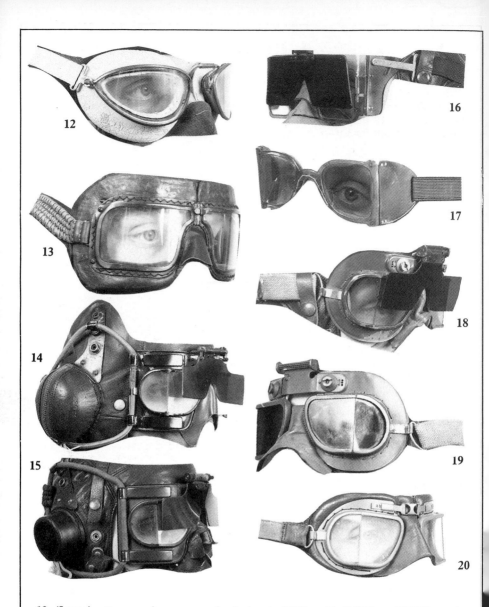

12. 'Luxor' pattern goggles, very popular during the 1930's. **13.** RAF issue MkIIIA goggles issue 1935–1942 stores reference No. 22C/62. **14.** WWII RAF issue MkIV pattern goggles, having elasticated side cords for fitting over ear phone covers plus side plate fastening. Note the flip up plastic tinted sun shield. **15.** WWII RAF issue MkIV goggles, identical to 14 except for the addition of a rear leather strap. **16.** WWII RAF issue MkVB goggles, a most unusual and unpopular item. Light green plastic frames with flip up sun shield and elasticated strap. **17.** WWII RAF issue MkVI sunglasses/goggles, equally short lived and unpopular issue item. **18.** RAF WWII pattern goggles with flip up sun shield. Issued 1942–43 period. **19.** RAF MkVIIA pattern, as 18 but with offically removed sun visor. **20.** RAF MkVIII goggles issued from 1944 through to 1970, this type was produced by a variety of manufacturers and also sold to the motorcyclists of the period by makers such as 'Stadium'.

9. PICTURES, PHOTOS AND PORTRAITS

Period photographs from both private albums and posed portraits can be perhaps the most rewarding area for collectors and historians. Photo postcards are also both informative and, of recent years, a good investment. A profusion of postcards were available some 10 years ago at between 25–50 pence each, many of these same postcards now sell for £10–£20 each.

1. A WWII Oil Painting on canvas of an RAF Chaplain of squadron-leader rank. A family crest is included to one corner. 2. WWI Oil Painting on canvas. A portrait of an RFC Air Mechanic, the painting is dated 1917 and is in the style of Holbein. 3. An evocative photo portrait of a Royal Flying Corps pilot, he epitomises the many young men who joined the RFC straight from school. Larger photo portraits of this quality are now quite scarce. 4. Small sepia-tone photo portrait of WWI RFC Airman complete with bronzed collar insignia and cap badge. 5. A good modern Oil painting depicting a Spad fighter of 'Escadrille Spa 48 1917'. 6. A WWI Photo portrait of an Officer. The frame mounts his cap badges of Sussex Yeomanry and RAF, both in bronzed finish. 7. An original pencil drawing of a 1920's period armoured car and 'Wapati' Aeroplane, by Michael Turner and featured in the book "RAF Illustrated". 8. Photo portrait in sepia-tone of an RFC Officer wearing side cap with 'maternity' tunic.

9

10

11

12

9. Autographed photo portrait of Lt. J. Alcock taken at Madros in 1916 whilst serving with No.2 wing RNAS. This Officer later found fame and was Knighted for his Atlantic flight with Lt. A.W. Brown in 1919. **10.** Unusual continental 'tapestry' portraits of early aviators, manufactured in France during the 1920's. **11.** Coloured print of WWI Aerial view of Ypres, depicting British Aircraft coming under Anti-Aircraft fire. This specially commissioned painting was produced in 1916. **12.** A Squadron crest, hand-painted onto Aircraft canvas, for Mess hall display or perhaps souvenir/presentation on the Squadrons disbandment in 1919. (16 sqn. formed at St. Omer, France – disbanded 31st Dec. 1919).

13

14

15　　　　　　　　　　　　　**16**

13. A period painting of the 'Battle of Britain' by Paul Nash. An impressive print which evokes the memories of this historic period.　**14.** Nazi N.S.F.K. Recruiting Poster. This organization trained and produced large numbers of Luftwaffe pilots and personnel when Germany was officially without an air-force.　**15.** An 'official' Nazi portrait of Reichsmarschall Hermann Goering shown wearing his famous wedding sword, carrying his baton and wearing the uniform of a Luftwaffe Generalfeldmarschall. This example is an 'Oleograph' (simulated oil painting) as found in Luftwaffe Head quarters and Squadron Mess buildings.　**16.** An autographed photo portrait of Hermann Goering wearing his unique uniform of Reichsmarschall. Note the Grand Cross of the Iron Cross, the 'Blue Max' and Knights Cross.

17

18

17. A modern oil painting on canvas of a WWII Bombing raid on Germany. These pictures are normally quite modestly priced and often prove a good investment. **18.** *Spitfires on Dawn Patrol*. Oil on canvas, modern.

19

20

19. 'Meteor jet fighter' circa 1950's. Oil on canvas, these paintings were often commissioned by the pilots and would include their aircraft markings, unit insignia etc. 20. 'Falklands War', oil painting of a Harrier on patrol over the Falklands. Painted by Dion Pears a popular aero artist. The Falklands conflict created a tremendous output of pictures and prints relating to the Harriers role in the war.

21. Wartime photo-portrait of a Nazi Luftwaffe senior N.C.O. 'Stabsfeldwebel'. He wears his white top summer issue cap and marksmans lanyard to his right shoulder. The badges to the left pocket are for membership to Nazi sports league 'D.R.L.' and the scarce 'Heavy Athletics Badge'. **22.** Wartime oil painting portrait of a Nazi Luftwaffe 'Oberleutnant' wearing combat style uniform tunic with belt and cross-strap. The only clue to his 'arm of service' would be by the collar and cap waffenfarbe (colour) red for Flak/artillery, yellow for flight service etc. **23.** Informal photo of Nazi 'ace' and Knights Cross recipient F.W. Willius of III/JG26, together with a British pilot he has just shot down. **24.** Photo portrait circa 1939 of William Pollard in the uniform of an officer of the Air Defence League. Pollard served in WWI with RNAS No2 wing at Madros, and later with the British Air Mission to Japan from 1920/21. He was awarded 'The Order of the Rising Sun'.

10. HEADWEAR, DRESS AND FLIGHT

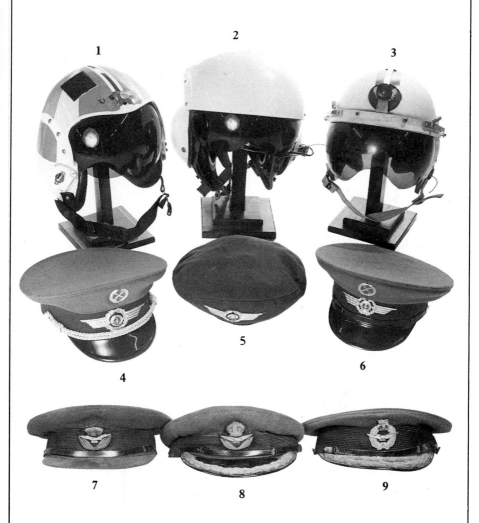

1. U.S. Marine Corps fighter pilots flight helmet, circa 1970, with twin visor (one plain, one tinted) and integral ear-phones. **2.** U.S. Army Air Force helicopter pilot's flying helmet of the Vietnam war era. It has dual sun visors, internal earphones and adjustable side hinge microphone. **3.** U.S. Airforce pilots helmet, type P-1B, of the Korean war era. It has an external hinge sun visor and integral ear-phones. **4.** 1980's pattern East German Airforce Officers peaked service Cap with enamelled centre motif and wire cap cords. **5.** Unusual beret, from a female auxiliary of the East German Airforce, made of grey wool with cotton embroidered insignia. **6.** 1980's pattern East German Airforce enlisted mans peaked service Cap in light grey, with dark grey cap band and cornflower blue piping (Waffen farbe). **7.** R.A.F. Officers peaked service Cap, circa 1930. **8.** R.A.F. Officers peaked service Cap of Group Captain rank with single row of embroidery to the peak. **9.** R.A.F. Air Commodore rank Officers peaked service Cap with double row of peaked embroidery and distinctive cap insignia, circa 1930.

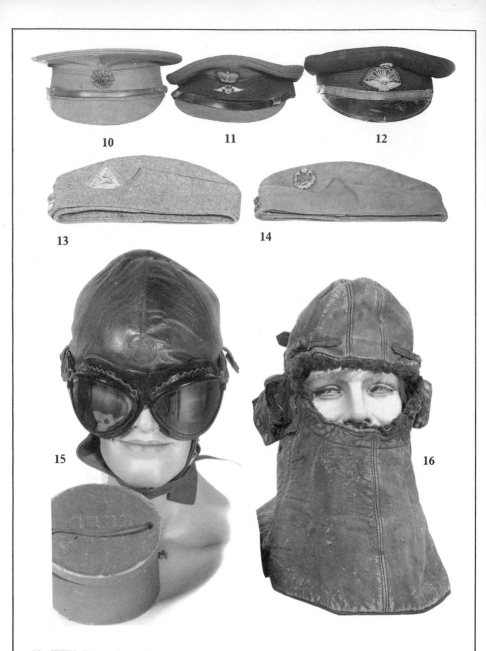

10. WWI Royal Flying Corps Officers Summer weight peaked service Cap with bronzed badge. **11.** RAF Chaplains peaked service Cap, circa 1960. **12.** 1920's Ocean Weather Service peaked Cap. **13.** WWII British Womans Jnr Air Corps side Cap of light grey with cotton embroidered insignia. **14.** Royal Flying Corps Officers side Cap with bronzed insignia. c.1917. **15.** Japanese WWII Army Air Force pilots brown leather flight helmet complete with Goggles and card case of issue. **16.** British WWI Royal Flying Corps "full face" hooded flying helmet of tan leather, fur lined with roll-back ear flaps.

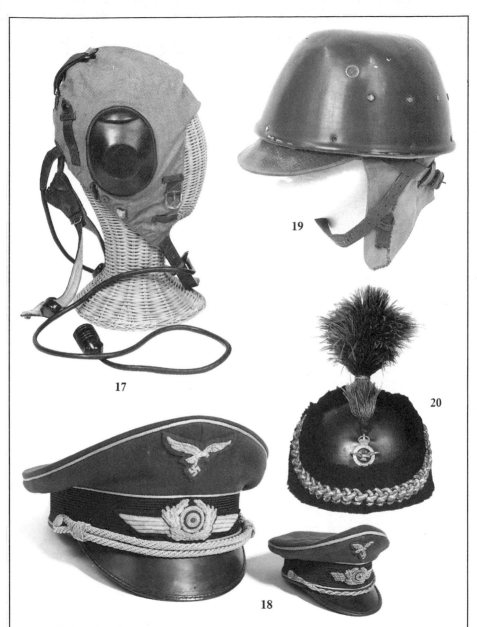

17. WWII Nazi Luftwaffe pilots Summer weight flight helmet. Of tan Gaberdine and brown leather trim it has a throat microphone and radio lead with 'jack' plug. **18.** Nazi Luftwaffe Officers full-dress peaked service Cap showing alloy wire embroidered insignia, Cap cords and waffen farbe, with a miniature version manufactured by the cap makers as an advertising novelty. **19.** Rare pre-war Nazi NSFK glider pilots training alloy helmet, painted in blue/grey with leather peak and canvas side straps. **20.** British RAF Officers full-dress ceremonial helmet in black leather with fur trim, blue and gold cording, silver and gilt cap badge and grey feather plume.

21   22

23

24

25

21. WWI German Air-ship Ratings cap of Naval pattern.   **22.** WWI German Sea plane unit Ratings Naval pattern service Cap.   **23.** WWI German Naval Land plane unit Ratings Cap.   **24.** Similar Cap of the 'Marine-Feldflieger'.   **25.** British Royal Flying Corps standard pattern flight helmet has fur trim with roll, flap ear covers and Mark I. type goggles.

26. British R.A.F. Mark I flying helmet in tan leather, with Mark 2 pattern Goggles.
27. British RAF 1939/41 'Battle of Britain' era, 'B' type, helmet with Mark IIIA goggles, 'D' type cloth and chamois-covered oxygen mask. **28.** British RAF 'C' type leather flight helmet with Mark VII goggles and 'G' type oxygen mask. **29.** RAF WWII Canvas Summer issue flight helmet with neck flap, Mark IVA goggles with hinge, sun visor and unusual pattern oxygen mask.

FOR THE COLLECTOR WHO HAS 'EVERYTHING'

A British RAF 'Fire streak' heat-seeking, infra-red homing, air-to-air guided missile. Capable of speeds over Mach 2, and used during the 1970's on Lightning Intercepter fighters and R.N. Sea/Vixen air-craft, a limited amount of these were released onto the UK market in the 1980's but with the proviso "not to be exported"!

VALUE £500–£800